EXCALIBUR

THE LEGEND OF
KING ARTHUR

EXCALIBUR

THE LEGEND OF
KING ARTHUR

A GRAPHIC NOVEL

WRITTEN BY
TONY LEE

ILLUSTRATED, COLORED, AND LETTERED
BY **SAM HART**

CANDLEWICK PRESS

Pendragon (Pen·dra·gən) (n)
Taken from the Welsh *pen*, meaning "head" and *draeg* meaning "dragon."

In ancient times, kings of Britons would inherit the epithet *Pendragon*, which referred to their status as a "supreme war chief" or "head dragon."

The name was misinterpreted by Geoffrey of Monmouth in the *Historia Regum Britanniae* to mean "dragon's head." According to Monmouth's writings, King Uther acquired the title of Pendragon when he witnessed a dragon-shaped comet, inspiring him to display dragons on all his war standards.

LONG AGO, *UTHER PENDRAGON* WAS KING, AND THE LAND OF ALBION WAS IN DISARRAY.

FOR UTHER WAS AT WAR WITH ANOTHER: *GORLOIS*, THE *DUKE OF CORNWALL*.

GORLOIS HAD SECRETLY MARRIED *IGRAINE*, UTHER'S FIRST LOVE, AND FATHERED A CHILD, *MORGANA*.

BETRAYED, UTHER WENT TO *WAR* WITH GORLOIS – A LONG AND BLOODY ONE THAT COVERED THE WHOLE OF ALBION.

DURING THE WAR, UTHER'S NEED FOR IGRAINE WAS SO *STRONG* THAT HE DEMANDED THAT THE WIZARD *MERLIN* HELP HIM *SEE* HER.

BUT MERLIN *REFUSED*. FURIOUS, UTHER *BANISHED* HIM FROM COURT, SAYING THAT HE WOULD FIND *ANOTHER* WAY.

AND HE *DID*. HE MADE AN ALLIANCE WITH THE *UNSEELIE COURT OF FAERIE*, ASKING *THEM* INSTEAD FOR THEIR HELP IN THIS TASK.

USING THEIR *GLAMOUR*, THEIR *DARK MAGICK*, THE UNSEELIE *DISGUISED* HIM AS GORLOIS, WHILE HIS TROOPS TRICKED THE *REAL* GORLOIS OUT OF THE CASTLE.

IGRAINE BELIEVED HE WAS HER *HUSBAND*, AND AS SUCH GAVE HIM *EVERYTHING*.

AND A MILE AWAY, GORLOIS WAS *KILLED* IN BATTLE.

WITH THE WAR OVER, UTHER AND IGRAINE *MARRIED*, AND IN TIME SHE GAVE BIRTH TO A BOY . . .

ARTHUR AP UTHER—ARTHUR, SON OF UTHER, ALSO KNOWN AS *ARTHUR PENDRAGON*.

AND UTHER WAS *SCARED*.

FOR THE COST OF THE DEAL HE MADE WITH THE UNSEELIE WAS THE CHILD OF HIS MARRIAGE –*ARTHUR.*

AND SO UTHER CALLED FOR MERLIN ONCE MORE, AND MERLIN *TOOK ARTHUR* FROM UTHER, NEVER TELLING THE KING WHERE THE CHILD WOULD BE HIDDEN.

WITH ARTHUR GONE, THE UNSEELIE COURT CLAIMED THAT UTHER HAD *CHEATED* THEM.

INSTEAD THEY DEMANDED *MORGANA,* UTHER'S STEP-DAUGHTER, TO BE HANDED OVER. AND UTHER RELUCTANTLY AGREED.

BUT THE DAMAGE WAS DONE; THE *TRUST WAS BROKEN* BETWEEN UTHER AND THE UNSEELIE FAE.

IN REVENGE, THE UNSEELIE COURT TURNED TO *LORD ULRIC,* KING UTHER'S CLOSEST FRIEND AND ADVISER, CONVINCING HIM TO *ENVY* HIS KING.

THEY ENCOURAGED ULRIC'S GREED FOR UTHER'S *CROWN,* AND ULRIC FOUGHT AND *DEFEATED* HIS KING AND ONETIME FRIEND.

UTHER DIED –

– BUT NOT BEFORE *THRUSTING HIS SWORD, CALIBURN, INTO A STONE,* STOPPING ULRIC FROM *TAKING IT* FOR HIMSELF.

WITH NO UTHER TO STOP HIM, ULRIC CROWNED HIMSELF *KING OF THE BRITONS.* BUT THE WIZARD MERLIN MADE A *PROPHECY* –

– THAT ONE DAY THE SWORD WOULD BE *PULLED,* AND THE *TRUE* KING OF ALBION WOULD RULE ONCE MORE.

HE WOULD *RULE* THE PEOPLE, HE WOULD *FIGHT* FOR THE PEOPLE . . .

ALBION, DURING THE REIGN OF *KING ULRIC*.

...DIE FOR THE PEOPLE...

ARTHUR!

ARTHUR! STOP *DAYDREAMING!* WE'VE GOT *VISITORS* APPROACHING!

I WASN'T *DAYDREAMING, CEI.* I WAS HAVING THAT *VISION* AGAIN.

THE ONE WHERE YOU'RE *LYING IN THE MUD?*

DAYDREAMING.

IT'S NOT A DREAM, CEI. I SEE MY *DEATH.* PEOPLE JUST DON'T *DREAM* THINGS LIKE THAT.

WHO'S COMING TO SEE US?

I'M NOT SURE. FATHER JUST SAID TO GET YOU, MAKE SURE YOU WERE THERE WHEN THEY ARRIVED.

WAIT — YOU DON'T THINK SIR ECTOR IS *APPRENTICING* ME, DO YOU?

DON'T *EVER* THINK THAT! MY FATHER LOVES YOU AS A *SON!*

OBVIOUSLY NOT AS MUCH AS ME, BUT THEN... I'M *BRILLIANT.* YOU MIGHT BE THE SON OF A KING, *ARTHUR AP UTHER,* BUT I HAVE *STYLE* AND *GRACE.*

AND I HAVE?

BLIND OPTIMISM AND *YOUTHFUL VIGOR,* WART.

THAT, AN *EARNEST SCOWL,* AND FAITH IN *EVERYONE.*

...KING OF THE BRITONS.

ECTOR! THERE YOU ARE! I THOUGHT YOU WERE *HIDING* FROM ME!

AND WHO ARE THESE?

THIS IS *CEI*, MY SON. THE YOUNGER ONE IS *ARTHUR*, CEI'S *SQUIRE*, LORD ULRIC.

YOU'RE ULRIC? THE MAN WHO KILLED *KING UTHER*, WHO DROVE HIS SWORD INTO THE STONE?

AYE, THAT'S ME. I KILLED UTHER BY THE BANKS OF THE *RIVER VER* –

– *BUT IT WAS UTHER* WHO SHEATHED CALIBURN IN STONE.

AND IT'S *KING* ULRIC, WHELP.

TEACH YOUR WARD SOME *MANNERS*, ECTOR – BEFORE HE GETS HIMSELF INTO TROUBLE.

CRACK!

AND TO WHAT DO WE OWE THIS *VISIT,* LORD KING? IT HAS BEEN *YEARS* SINCE YOU GRACED THIS HEARTH.

AYE, OVER TEN YEARS OR MORE, BY MY RECKONING. BUT FUNNILY ENOUGH, THE BOY MENTIONS THE WAY OF IT.

I'M HERE ABOUT THE *SWORD.*

EVERY YEAR SINCE I PUT DOWN THAT *RABID DOG UTHER,* THE PEOPLE OF THIS LAND GATHER TOGETHER TO TRY TO *PULL* CALIBURN FROM THE STONE.

EVERY YEAR, YOUNG MEN ARRIVE AT *STONE HILL* AND TRY TO SHOW THAT *THEY* ARE THE TRUE KING OF ALBION.

MY KINGSHIP. *MY* BRITONS. *MY* ALBION.

THIS IS AN *AFFRONT TO MY RULE,* ECTOR. *OPEN TREASON.* THEY USE THE SWORD AS A MEANS TO REPLACE ME.

NOT *THIS* YEAR. SPREAD THE WORD, LORD. TELL THEM TO KEEP AWAY THIS SPRING EQUINOX. TO RESIST IS *DEATH.*

PERHAPS IF YOU PULLED THE SWORD *YOURSELF?* THAT WAY THEY'D ALL SEE WHO'S REALLY KING!

I NEED NO *MAGIC SWORD* TO RULE THIS NATION OF FOOLS. I'VE DONE WELL ENOUGH THESE LAST TEN YEARS WITHOUT IT.

SPREAD THE WORD, ECTOR. *NO MERCY* FOR THOSE WHO IGNORE THIS DECREE.

DID YOU HEAR THAT? *"DECREE."* ULRIC'S LEARNED A NEW WORD.

THAT MUST HAVE TAKEN SOME DOING.

WHAT DO WE DO, FATHER?

NOTHING. EVEN IF WE TELL THEM, THE PEOPLE WILL STILL GO TO STONE HILL.

ALL WE CAN DO IS *WARN THEM* THAT ULRIC WILL BE WATCHING.

BUT FATHER! WHAT ABOUT ARTHUR? HE NEEDS TO LEARN HOW TO *DEFEND* HIMSELF IF HE'S TO BE *KING* –

HE WILL NOT LEARN SWORDPLAY WHILE UNDER MY ROOF!

I MAY HAVE OWED MERLIN ENOUGH TO TAKE ARTHUR IN, BUT I'LL BE *DAMNED* IF I HELP THAT WIZARD DRAG THE BOY TO AN EARLY GRAVE!

HE WILL HAVE TIME TO LEARN SWORDPLAY *AFTER* HE IS CROWNED! *NOT WHILE HE IS A BOY!*

NO SWORDPLAY, EH?

LOOKS LIKE IT, WART.

WE'D BETTER NOT TELL HIM WHAT YOU'VE BEEN *TEACHING* ME, THEN.

THAT *MIGHT* BE A PLAN.

CEI?

OH, *THANK GOD!* IT WAS LIKE YOU WERE POSSESSED! YOU WERE GOING TO *KILL* ME!

I WOULD NEVER DO THAT. YOU'RE MY *BROTHER!*

BUT, I DIDN'T EVEN KNOW THAT I *WAS* FIGHTING YOU. ALL I SAW WAS THAT VISION AGAIN.

THAT VISION MIGHT BE *YOUR* DEATH, BUT IT WAS ALMOST *MY DEATH* THEN!

WE SHOULD STOP THIS. I KNOW YOU THINK I SHOULD KNOW HOW TO *USE* A SWORD—

—BUT I WON'T EVEN *TOUCH* CALIBURN FOR ALMOST A MONTH, LET ALONE *PULL* IT. AND WHO KNOWS WHAT'LL HAPPEN AFTER THAT!

THAT'S *EASY.* YOU'LL DEFEAT *ULRIC* AND TAKE THE *CROWN.* AND FOR THAT YOU NEED TO KNOW HOW TO *FIGHT.*

COME ON, IT'LL BE SUPPER SOON. WE CAN PRACTICE AGAIN TOMORROW.

WE STILL HAVE *THREE WEEKS* UNTIL THE EQUINOX!

YES, YOUNG ARTHUR— *PRACTICE.* IN THREE WEEKS YOU STAND AT STONE HILL.

WAR IS COMING TO ALBION, MY KING—

—AND YOU MUST BE PREPARED FOR *BATTLE.*

OF **COURSE** THEY WON'T! BUT WHEN THEY **DARE** TO SHOW THEIR FACES AT STONE HILL —

— WE WILL **KILL EVERY LAST ONE OF THEM.**

"DO YOU THINK THEY WILL **LISTEN,** LORD KING?"

WHAT I DO NOT UNDERSTAND, KING ULRIC, IS WHY THIS BOTHERS YOU **NOW?**

FOR **TEN YEARS** YOU'VE LET THEM HAVE THEIR JOUSTS, THEIR **FAYRE.** YOU'VE LET THEM HAVE THEIR FUTILE ATTEMPTS TO PULL OUT THE SWORD.

BECAUSE THIS YEAR THE SWORD IS **DESTINED** TO BE PULLED.

AND I **WILL NOT** HAVE THAT HAPPEN.

HOW DO YOU **KNOW** THIS?

WHEN I KILLED UTHER, I TOOK HIS FAMILY AS MINE. BUT HIS STEPDAUGHTER WAS **MISSING,** TAKEN FIVE YEARS EARLIER BY THE FAE.

UTHER FAILED IN A BARGAIN, YOU SEE. HE HID HIS **SON** AND GAVE HIS **STEPDAUGHTER** TO THE DARK FAE AS PAYMENT.

TEN YEARS SHE SPENT IN THE **FAERIE REALM.** WHEN SHE FINALLY RETURNED, SHE TOLD ME OF A **PROPHECY** ABOUT THE SWORD — AND ITS WIELDER.

SHE CALLS HERSELF **MORGANA LE FEY** — MORGANA OF THE FAE. SHE KNOWS THE **MAGICK** OF THE UNSEELIE COURT —

— AND SHE SAYS THAT CALIBURN **WILL** BE PULLED FREE IN **THREE WEEKS.**

CEI! WE DON'T HAVE THE *TIME* FOR THIS!

OF *COURSE* WE DO, FATHER! WE NEED TO HAVE HIM TRY THE SWORD *BEFORE* ULRIC ARRIVES!

TRY THE SWORD? YOU MEAN I'M SUPPOSED TO PULL IT NOW?

RIGHT NOW?

ULRIC'S *BOUND* TO ARRIVE AT SOME POINT TODAY –

– SO BEFORE HE COMES TO SPOIL THE PARTY, YOU NEED TO *PROVE* YOU'RE THE *ONCE AND FUTURE KING.*

"THERE'S NO BETTER TIME THAN RIGHT NOW FOR THE *SWORD IN THE STONE.*"

MAKE WAY! THIS IS THE BOY'S *FIRST TIME* WITH THE SWORD!

NEWCOMER TO THE BLADE!

IF MERLIN TOLD THE *TRUTH,* ARTHUR, *YOU'RE* THE ONE TO PULL THIS BLADE.

THIS IS YOUR MOMENT. THE PROPHECY STATES THAT ONLY THE *TRUE KING,* WITH THE *NEED,* CAN PULL THE BLADE.

THE LAND IS IN *TURMOIL.* ULRIC IS A *TYRANT.* WE HAVE *NEVER* NEEDED IT MORE, ARTHUR. *FREE THE BLADE. SAVE THE PEOPLE.*

THIS IS YOUR *DESTINY,* ARTHUR. THIS IS YOUR *SWORD.* HELP THE PEOPLE. PULL THE BLADE. . . .

GRAAGGHH!!!

BUT – I DON'T *UNDERSTAND!* MERLIN SAID...

I'VE TOLD YOU BEFORE, CEI – MERLIN *LIES.* THE PROPHECY WAS *WRONG.*

WHY SHOULD WE LISTEN TO A MAN WHO *LEFT ME ON A DOORSTEP?*

AH WELL, WART – YOU *TRIED.* I'M SURE THE PROPECY ALLOWS FOR THIS ... *SURPRISE.*

HELL, IT JUST MEANS WE GET YOU FOR ANOTHER YEAR OR SO BEFORE YOUR HEAD GETS *BIGGER,* "YOUR *MAJESTY.*"

IF IT DOES, IT'S ONLY BECAUSE I'M FOLLOWING *YOUR* LEAD.

AND A FINE LEAD IT IS! NOW YOU GET TO DO SOMETHING EVEN *BETTER* THAN BEING KING!

YOU GET TO BE THE *SQUIRE* TO THE *MIGHTY CEI!*

WHY, IS THERE SOMEONE *ELSE* WITH YOUR NAME?

RUN! TAKE COVER!

ULRIC'S HERE!

ULRIC! ULRIC!

ULRIC! ULRIC!

SWISHH!

GRARGHH!!!

ARTHUR! GET *LORD LEODEGRANCE* AND HIS DAUGHTER TO SAFETY!

I'M GOING TO *HELP FATHER!* HE'S GONE UP AGAINST ULRIC!

WHACK!

ULRIC! DAMN YOU!

SO! THE *BOY* WANTS TO PLAY AT BEING A MAN!

CEI! NO! *STAY BACK!*

THE **SWORD** — IT FEELS SO LIGHT, LIKE IT'S A **PART** OF ME!

UTHER?

HE PULLED **CALIBURN!** HE PULLED THE BLADE!

WHO IS HE? IS HE UTHER **RETURNED?**

A **KING!** WE HAVE A **KING! ALBION** IS SAVED!

WAIT, THE PROPHECY WAS **TRUE?**

MERLIN WAS **RIGHT?** I CAN'T BELIEVE THAT **MERLIN WAS TELLING THE TRUTH** FOR ONCE!

YOU'RE **DAMNED RIGHT** ABOUT THAT, BOY. **I'M** THE KING OF ALBION. **I'M** THE KING OF THE BRITONS.

NOW **GIVE ME THAT SWORD!**

HEAR ME, ULRIC OF ALBION! *THE SWORD HAS BEEN PULLED!*

TO DEMAND IT IS AN ACT OF *CHALLENGE* AND WILL BE *TREATED* AS SUCH!

MERLIN! I SHOULD HAVE KNOWN THAT THIS WOULD BE ONE OF YOUR *GAMES!* I'M NOT PLAYING!

AH, ARTHUR, SO GOOD TO SEE YOU.

AND THIS *ISN'T* A GAME, BOY. THIS IS *DEATHLY* SERIOUS.

THE BOY IS *ARTHUR PENDRAGON*, THE SON OF *UTHER* PENDRAGON, AND, AS SUCH, CLAIMS THE MANTLE OF KINGSHIP BY *HERITAGE* AND *RIGHT.*

YOU CAN CHALLENGE FOR IT TOMORROW MORNING AT *DAWN.* DO YOU ACCEPT?

AYE, I'LL RETURN TOMORROW AT DAWN. I'LL *KILL* YOUR BOY –

– AND *TAKE BACK* MY KINGDOM, WIZARD.

YAHH!

I HAVE TO FIGHT *ULRIC* TOMORROW?

AT DAWN, YES. WON'T THAT BE *FUN?* I'M SURE YOU'RE *VERY* EXCITED –

– BUT WE HAVE A LOT TO *DO* BEFORE THEN.

THIS IS **BRAN THE BLESSED**, THE RULER OF AVALON. HE HAS AGREED TO LET YOU TRAIN HERE. AND HE WILL DEBATE WITH YOU THE LAWS OF KINGSHIP.

YOU ARE WELCOME HERE, ARTHUR PENDRAGON. AS WAS YOUR MOTHER, **IGRAINE**.

YOU KNEW MY MOTHER?

OF COURSE! YOUR MOTHER WAS A **HALF FAE PRINCESS** OF THE **SEELIE COURT**.

SHE WAS ONE OF THE REASONS WHY THE **UNSEELIE COURT** WANTED YOU WHEN YOU WERE BORN.

THIS IS **BERTILAK**, THE **GREEN KNIGHT**, CHAMPION OF THE SEELIE COURT.

WITH HIS AIDES **BALAN** AND **BALIN**, HE WILL TEACH YOU THE ART OF FIGHTING.

SEELIE, UNSEELIE — WHAT DO THESE WORDS **MEAN**?

THERE ARE TWO SIDES TO FAERIE: **SEELIE** AND **UNSEELIE**. DAY AND NIGHT. SUMMER AND WINTER.

YOU LEARN FROM THE SEELIE, THE "LIGHT" SIDE OF FAERIE. BE VERY WARY OF THE "DARK" SIDE.

AND FINALLY, THIS IS **VIVIANNE**, THE **LADY OF THE LAKE**.

SHE WILL BE YOUR ADVISER, YOUR TUTOR IN THE WAYS OF **FAERIE** WHILE YOU ARE HERE.

HELLO, ARTHUR.

I — UM, HELLO. I MEAN . . .

WOW.

YES, SHE **HAS** THAT AFFECT ON PEOPLE.

COME ON, ARTHUR. YOU HAVE A LOT TO LEARN AND ONLY A **YEAR AND A DAY** TO DO IT IN. LET'S GET STARTED.

AS NIGHT PASSED IN THE MORTAL WORLD, ARTHUR TRAINED FOR *A YEAR AND A DAY* IN AVALON.

AND THE PEOPLE OF FAERIE TAUGHT HIM THE *ART OF KINGSHIP*...

...THE TACTICS OF *WAR CRAFT*...

...THE WAYS OF *POLITICS*...

...AND THE JOYS OF *FRIENDSHIP*.

IT'S NOT AS IF THIS WAS A *QUICK* DECISION. EVEN THOUGH IT'S BEEN *HOURS* IN ALBION, WE'VE BEEN HERE ALMOST A *YEAR*, NOW.

I MEAN IT, MERLIN, I THINK I'M IN *LOVE* WITH HER.

VIVIANNE? SHE'S OLD ENOUGH TO BE YOUR . . .

WELL, THAT IS, SHE'S *QUITE OLD*, YOU KNOW.

I KNOW, BUT IN A WEEK I FINISH MY TRAINING AND WE RETURN. AND I MIGHT *NEVER SEE HER* AGAIN!

WHAT DO I DO? DO I *TELL* HER?

IN A WEEK WE DO INDEED RETURN, AND AT THAT POINT YOU NEED TO BE *FOCUSED*.

ADOLESCENT ACTS OF *LOVE* CAN WAIT UNTIL ULRIC IS DEFEATED.

SPOKEN LIKE A MAN WHO'S NEVER *BEEN* IN LOVE.

OH, HE'S BEEN IN LOVE, YOUNG MAN. *BELIEVE* ME.

NIMUE!

HELLO, MERLIN. I THOUGHT YOU'D GONE. I'M SO *GLADDENED* THAT YOU HAVEN'T.

CAN WE . . . MAY WE WALK *ALONE* FOR A WHILE? I'VE MISSED YOU SO.

OH, OF COURSE!

WE'LL SPEAK ABOUT THIS *LATER*, ARTHUR. YOU'RE LATE FOR YOUR SESSION WITH *BERTILAK*.

GREAT. THANKS.

FOR *NOTHING*.

DID YOU **MEAN** WHAT YOU SAID JUST THEN, ARTHUR?

THAT YOU **LOVED** ME?

WHAT? OH NO, YOU **HEARD**?

I'M TOUCHED, HONORED EVEN. BUT IT CAN **NEVER** BE.

YOU'RE A **BOY**, NOT YET SIXTEEN, AND I — WELL, I AM MUCH, **MUCH** OLDER.

AGE SHOULDN'T **MATTER!** I KNOW THAT WE COULD WORK THINGS OUT!

AND EACH DAY I GROW **OLDER**, WHILE YOU STAY THE SAME! SOON WE'LL BE **SIMILAR** IN LOOKS AND THOUGHT!

AND ON THAT DAY, I'LL **LISTEN** TO YOU ABOUT THIS. BUT CURRENTLY? YOU'RE A BOY. AND MY STUDENT.

AND BESIDES, WE BOTH KNOW THAT YOU'RE GOING TO BE A MIGHTY KING AND WILL MARRY A PRINCESS, HAVE A LONG AND HAPPY LIFE . . .

THE KING WOULD DIE FOR THE PEOPLE.

I — I KNOW.

IT'S JUST THAT — FOR **ONE** DAY . . .

. . . I WANTED TO **FORGET** MY DESTINY.

YOUNG ARTHUR, IT HAS BEEN A PLEASURE TO MEET YOU AND WATCH YOU *GROW* THIS LAST YEAR.

AND NOW, AS YOU RETURN TO YOUR *OWN* WORLD, WE HOPE THAT YOU HAVE THE STRENGTH—

—AND THE *WILL* TO DEFEAT YOUR FOE AND RESTORE ALBION TO ITS FORMER *GLORY.* DO YOU HAVE ANY FINAL WORDS BEFORE YOU LEAVE?

I'M—I'M *NOT READY,* MY LORD. I NEED *ANOTHER YEAR.*

WHAT? ANOTHER YEAR AND A DAY? THIS *WASN'T* ASKED BY *YOU,* MERLIN!

ARTHUR, WHAT ARE YOU *DOING!* ANOTHER YEAR AND A DAY WOULD BRING US PERILOUSLY CLOSE TO ARRIVING *AFTER* THE DAWN!

AND IF WE ARRIVE TOO LATE, *WE FORFEIT THE DUEL!*

ONE MORE YEAR. ONE MORE YEAR FOR YOU TO SEE *NIMUE.*

ONE MORE YEAR FOR ME TO BE WITH *VIVIANNE* BEFORE I HAVE TO LEAVE. BEFORE I HAVE TO *GROW UP.*

MERLIN DIDN'T MAKE THIS ARRANGEMENT, LORD KING, BECAUSE THIS IS *MY* ARRANGEMENT.

GIVE ME WHATEVER *TERMS* YOU WANT. I WILL STAND BY THEM.

YOU BEG A *FAVOR FROM A FAERIE?* THAT IS A DANGEROUS ROUTE, BOY.

BUT I *LIKE* THAT. VERY WELL. A YEAR AND A DAY MORE. HOWEVER, THERE IS A *CLAUSE* IN THIS DEAL.

AFTER YOU HAVE FINISHED RULING THE BRITONS, YOU WILL RETURN HERE AND *TAKE MY PLACE* AS THE RULER OF *AVALON.*

WHAT?

ONCE A CENTURY I MUST *TRAVEL THE REALMS OF FAERIE.* AND I WILL NEED A *TRUSTWORTHY MAN* TO RULE IN MY ABSENCE.

WHAT DO YOU SAY, ARTHUR? WILL YOU RULE MY KINGDOM *AFTER* YOURS?

THE KING WOULD DIE FOR THE PEOPLE.

I—I WILL DO MY *BEST,* YOUR MAJESTY.

IF I STILL *LIVE* AT THE END.

STONE HILL, ALBION.

THIS IS MADNESS. CHILD OF LUTHER OR NOT –

–WE CANNOT ALLOW A **BOY** TO FIGHT ULRIC! HE'LL BE **KILLED!**

AS MUCH AS I DISLIKE HIM FOR USING ME IN HIS GAMES, MERLIN IS **ALWAYS** RIGHT. IF HE HAS A PLAN THAT ENSURES A WIN –

–THEN A WIN **WILL** HAPPEN.

AND WHAT IF HE **DOES** FAIL? ULRIC HAS THE **SWORD,** AND PROCLAIMS HIMSELF THE **RIGHTFUL RULER?**

WE'LL ALL BE PUT TO DEATH! HE WON'T ALLOW US TO GO FREE!

WE NEED TO PREPARE TO **FIGHT!** TO STOP ULRIC BEFORE HE GETS TO WART – I MEAN **ARTHUR!**

I AGREE, SIR CEI! WE MUST DEFEND OURSELVES **BEFORE** ULRIC ATTACKS!

DEFEND OURSELVES **BEFORE** HE ATTACKS? ISN'T THAT CALLED "ATTACKING FIRST"?

YOU COULD SEE IT THAT WAY, YES! BUT WE WOULD **SECURE** ARTHUR'S THRONE BEFORE HE RETURNS!

AND THEN PERHAPS WE CAN ARRANGE A **ROYAL WEDDING,** EH? AFTER ALL, ARTHUR WILL NEED A QUEEN!

FATHER, HE MAY HAVE SAVED MY LIFE – BUT ARTHUR PENDRAGON IS STILL A **BOY.** . . .

ULRIC'S CAMP.

SHOULDN'T YOU BE SLEEPING, SIRE? IT'S GOING TO BE A LONG DAY TOMORROW.

CAN'T YOUR WOMAN PAINT *PRETTY PICTURES* ON YOU THEN?

YOU *MORON!* THESE ARE *SIGILS OF POWER!* THE VERY *GLAMOUR* OF THE *DARK FAE THEMSELVES!*

WITH THESE ON, ULRIC WILL BE FASTER, STRONGER *BETTER* THAN ARTHUR. HE WILL NOT *NEED* TO SLEEP TONIGHT!

YES, THE *FIFTEEN-YEAR-OLD BOY.*

THE SKINNY, *SCARED* ONE. SUCH A FORMIDABLE OPPONENT.

WHO ALSO WIELDS *CALIBURN* AND HAS BEEN TAKEN *GOD KNOWS WHERE* FOR THE NIGHT BY MERLIN.

SO YES, I *WILL* TAKE ANY ADVANTAGE I CAN! NOW *GET OUT!*

IF THIS ARTHUR *IS* THE SON OF UTHER –

– THEN HE IS YOUR *HALF BROTHER.* WHY DO YOU *HATE* HIM SO?

BECAUSE WHEN I WAS FOUR, THE *UNSEELIE COURT* TOOK ME AWAY AS PART OF A *BARGAIN* WITH UTHER.

TEN YEARS I SPENT UNDER THEIR TUTELAGE. TEN DARK, *PAIN-FILLED* YEARS.

THEY TOOK ME *INSTEAD* OF THE ONE THEY CAME FOR, BECAUSE *MERLIN* HAD STOLEN HIM AWAY.

THEY TOOK *ME* INSTEAD OF *ARTHUR.*

IT SEEMS SO *STRANGE* THAT YOU MUST LEAVE US NOW, ARTHUR.

THAT YOU HAVE TO MOVE ON FROM US AND LIVE YOUR *REAL* LIFE ONCE MORE.

THIS IS MY REAL LIFE, VIVIANNE – AND TO LEAVE HERE, TO LEAVE *YOU* – WILL *TEAR MY HEART IN TWO.*

IN MY VISIONS I KNOW WHERE MY PATH *FINALLY LEADS*. BUT KNOW THIS, LADY OF THE LAKE.

I WILL *NEVER* LOVE ANOTHER AS I *LOVE YOU.*

AND I WILL NEVER LOVE ANOTHER AS I LOVE *YOU*, ARTHUR AP UTHER PENDRAGON OF ALBION.

YOU ARE NO LONGER A BOY. AND NOW YOU MUST GO.

THANK YOU. TO *ALL* OF YOU. WITHOUT YOUR HELP, I WOULD BE WALKING TO CERTAIN DEATH.

I JUST HOPE I *LIVE UP* TO YOUR TEACHINGS.

ARTHUR? ARE YOU ALL RIGHT?

JUST GET ME OUT OF HERE, MERLIN. I DON'T KNOW HOW LONG I CAN HOLD MYSELF STRAIGHT.

IT DOESN'T MATTER *WHAT* ULRIC DOES TODAY – WHETHER I SAVE ALBION OR NOT.

BY LEAVING VIVIANNE, I'VE *ALREADY LOST.*

STONE HILL.

DAMN *IT!* WHERE *IS* THAT WIZARD! HE PROMISED ARTHUR WOULD BE HERE *WELL* BEFORE THE DAWN!

HE'LL *BE* HERE, FATHER. EVEN IF MERLIN'S PLANS GO AWRY, ARTHUR HAS *NEVER* LET US DOWN!

ULRIC HAS ARRIVED! HE CLAIMS THAT THE DAWN IS BUT MOMENTS AWAY —

— AND IF *ARTHUR* DOESN'T APPEAR, HE WILL CLAIM THE DUEL BY *FORFEIT!*

THEN WE MUST *FIGHT.* STRIKE HIM NOW.

WE'LL NEVER GET ANOTHER CHANCE. MERLIN. . . .

AND WHAT ABOUT MERLIN, CEI? NEVER *FORGET,* BOY —

— *MERLIN AMBROSIUS ALWAYS* KEEPS HIS WORD.

DAWN.

FOR *ALBION!*

FOR THE *KING* IS THE LAND!

YOUR LAND IS IN *WINTER,* ULRIC . . .

WAIT . . .

WAIT? IS THAT WHAT MY *FATHER* BEGGED OF YOU?

BEFORE YOU *KILLED* HIM?

PLEASE, I BEG YOU . . .

YOU *BEG* ME NOW? YOU WANT *MERCY?*

DID YOU GIVE MY *FATHER* MERCY? HAVE YOU GIVEN THE *PEOPLE OF ALBION* MERCY?

NO! YOU STRUCK HIM DOWN! YOU *KILLED* HIM!

AND NOW THE *SON* HAS RETURNED TO SEEK *REVENGE!*

THE *SWORD IN THE STONE* MUST BE *SHEATHED* ONCE MORE.

SHUNK

YOU *LOST*, ULRIC. YIELD.

YIELD TO THE *NEW KING OF THE BRITONS*.

EVEN THOUGH YOU KILLED MY FATHER, I *WON'T* KILL YOU.

GO HOME. GATHER WHAT YOU CAN CARRY AND *LEAVE* ALBION. YOU ARE *BANISHED FOREVER* FROM ITS LANDS.

THIS ISN'T *OVER*, BOY! WHEN I—

YES IT IS, ULRIC. YOU CHALLENGED AND *LOST*.

AND BY THE *OLD LAWS*, *ANYONE* CAN CLAIM YOUR HEAD AS A *KEEPSAKE*. I SUGGEST YOU LEAVE BEFORE *I* CHOOSE TO.

MORGANA, YOUR DARK GLAMOUR DIDN'T HELP HIM.

IN FACT, IF ANYTHING, IT *WEAKENED* HIM. WHY WOULD YOU DO SUCH A THING?

OH, MERLIN, YOU'RE SO *BLIND*. I MIGHT HATE YOU AND ARTHUR FOR WHAT YOU DID TO ME . . .

. . . BUT HE'S STILL MY *BLOOD*. AND *BLOOD* IS STRONGER THAN *ANYTHING*.

I'LL BE *SEEING* YOU, WIZARD.

SHE *HELPED* ME, DIDN'T SHE? THAT WAS MORGANA, MY HALF SISTER, WASN'T IT?

YES, IT WAS. AND YES—

—FOR SOME UNKNOWN REASON SHE DID *INDEED* ASSIST YOU TODAY. BUT BEWARE—IT'LL BE A *FAVOR* SHE'LL CLAIM BACK.

YOU MENTIONED HER IN PASSING WHILE WE WERE IN *AVALON.* YOU SAID YOU WOULD TELL ME HER STORY WHEN I WAS *READY.*

I THINK I'M READY *NOW,* MERLIN.

THEN I WILL TELL YOU IT TONIGHT. *AFTER* THE FEAST. BECAUSE THERE *WILL BE* ONE, YOU KNOW.

YOUR *MAJESTY!* I DON'T KNOW WHETHER I SHOULD *HUG YOU* OR *KNEEL!*

THE MESSENGERS HAVE BEEN SENT OUT. SOON THE *WHOLE OF ALBION* WILL KNOW WE HAVE A *NEW KING!*

AND TONIGHT WE SHALL CELEBRATE IN MY CASTLE AT *CAMELIARD!*

TOLD YOU.

MY LORD, YESTERDAY I THOUGHT YOU WERE A *BOY.* I WANTED TO APOLOGIZE....

WHY? TO YOU, YESTERDAY I *WAS* A BOY.

NOW STOP TROUBLING OUR NEW *KING,* GUINEVERE. I'M SURE YOU'LL BE SEEING EACH OTHER *MUCH MORE* IN THE FUTURE!

MAYBE EVEN IN A MORE *WEDDING-RELATED MANNER,* EH?

NOW! TO CAMELIARD! TO A *FEAST!*

YOU ARE OUR GUEST UNTIL YOUR CASTLE IS BUILT, MY KING.

AND WE WILL TAKE ULRIC'S CASTLE DOWN, *STONE BY STONE*, TO MAKE YOUR NEW CAMELOT!

I STILL DON'T KNOW WHY I CAN'T JUST TAKE ULRIC'S CASTLE AS IT IS!

BECAUSE HE'LL MOST LIKELY HAVE PLACED *TRAPS* EVERYWHERE!

HE'LL *NEVER* ALLOW YOU TO BE KING IN *HIS* CASTLE— AND LIVE TO TELL THE TALE!

WE NEED TO DO SOMETHING ABOUT THESE *LONG TABLES*, ARTHUR!

WE'LL NEVER HEAR *ANYTHING* WHEN WE MEET!

YES, TABLES . . .

I'M SORRY, WILL YOU *EXCUSE ME* FOR A MOMENT?

MERLIN! WHERE ARE YOU GOING?

WE'VE BEEN TOGETHER IN *AVALON* FOR SO LONG. YOU *CAN'T* LEAVE ME NOW!

YOU'LL BE FINE. ECTOR AND CEI ARE HERE. AND LEODEGRANCE WILL LET YOU STAY UNTIL YOUR *CAMELOT* IS BUILT IN A YEAR OR TWO.

YOU HAVE HAD TWO BUSY YEARS, MY KING. TAKE THE TIME TO RELAX A LITTLE.

I'M GOING TO SPEAK WITH MORGANA BEFORE SHE LEAVES WITH ULRIC.

I NEED TO KNOW WHAT HER *PLANS* ARE. WHETHER SHE'S *FOR* OR *AGAINST* US.

YOU PROMISED THAT YOU WOULD *TELL ME* ABOUT HER AFTER THE FEAST.

WOULD THAT BE BEFORE OR *AFTER* YOU SKULKED OFF INTO THE NIGHT?

TRUE. I DID, DIDN'T I? THEN WALK WITH ME AND I'LL TELL YOU THE *TALE OF MORGANA.*

LONG AGO, *UTHER PENDRAGON* WAS KING, AND THE LAND WAS IN DISARRAY. . . .

THANK YOU FOR TELLING ME, MERLIN. ALL MY LIFE I *HATED* YOU, BELIEVING THAT YOU SIMPLY STOLE ME FROM MY FATHER FOR *PETTY REVENGE.*

BUT BEFORE YOU GO, I NEED ONE FAVOR FROM YOU.

YOU DO? WHAT IS IT, MY KING?

THEY WANT ME TO MARRY LEODEGRANCE'S DAUGHTER, *GUINEVERE.* IT'S NOT BEEN SAID YET, BUT IT WILL BE.

YET ALL I WANT IS VIVIANNE. ALL I *LOVE* IS VIVIANNE –

– AND EVERY SECOND I'M AWAY FROM HER *KILLS ME THAT LITTLE PIECE MORE.* I BEG YOU, HELP ME.

YOU KNOW WHAT YOU *ASK* OF ME? YOU'RE SURE OF THIS?

I AM. REMOVE MY MEMORIES OF MY *LOVE* FOR *THE LADY OF THE LAKE.*

LEAVE ME MY TIME IN AVALON, JUST *NOT VIVIANNE.* OTHERWISE I AM NO GOOD AS A KING TO THESE PEOPLE.

"DREAM, MY KING."

"DREAM – AND FORGET."

STATE YOUR NAME AND PURPOSE!

I AM SIMPLY *MERLIN,* GOOD MAN. AND I AM HERE TO SEE THE LADY MORGANA.

IF YOU COULD TELL HER . . .

NO NEED. SHE'S BEEN *EXPECTING* YOU.

SHE HAS?

MY LADY MORGANA . . .

AH, MERLIN, *THERE* YOU ARE.

YOU'RE *HALF AN HOUR LATE.*

WHAT ARE YOUR **PLANS**, MORGANA? WHY DID YOU SET ULRIC UP FOR A FALL?

YOU **HATE** ARTHUR. YOU HATE ME. SO WHY **HELP** HIM BECOME **KING**?

WHY NOT? ULRIC WAS A FOOL, ANYWAY. AND TO MAKE ARTHUR KING –

–ALL THE BETTER A DROP WHEN HE **FALLS.**

I CAN'T LET YOU DO THAT, MORGANA. ARTHUR IS TOO **IMPORTANT** TO THE PEOPLE OF ALBION.

THEY **NEED** HIM, AFTER YEARS OF ULRIC'S TYRANNY. AND IF I HAVE TO STOP YOU BY **FORCE,** I WILL.

OH, MERLIN, I DO SO **LOVE** IT WHEN YOU TRY TO ACT LIKE A **MAN.**

STOP ME BY FORCE? I WAS **HOPING** YOU'D SAY THAT.

– NOW DIE!

BZZAAPP!

IS THAT THE **BEST** YOU HAVE, MORGANA?

IS THAT ALL THE UNSEELIE COURT **GAVE** YOU?

OW. THAT *HURT.*

DAMN YOU, MORGANA.

SNOW? BUT IT WAS *SPRINGTIME!*

WHERE HAVE YOU SENT ME, WITCH?

HO THERE! *YOU, SIR!*

HELP A MAN IN DISTRESS? PLEASE?

BLOW ME! *MERLIN THE MAGICIAN!* I THOUGHT YOU WERE DEAD!

I ALMOST WAS.

WAIT — YOU *KNOW* ME? WHERE AM I?

WHERE *ARE* YOU? WHY, YOU'RE IN THE KINGDOM OF ALBION, NEXT TO THE MIGHTY *CAMELOT ITSELF!*

CAMELOT? IT CAN'T BE. ARTHUR HAD ONLY JUST STARTED TO *TALK* ABOUT SUCH A CASTLE!

AYE, HE TALKED FOR ABOUT A YEAR, AND THEN IT TOOK ANOTHER *THREE* TO BUILD.

BUT FOR THE LAST *THREE YEARS* HE'S LIVED THERE –

– *KING ARTHUR OF CAMELOT.*

...*SEVEN YEARS?*

PLEASE, TELL ME, WHAT *ELSE* HAS HAPPENED IN THE LAST SEVEN YEARS?

THINGS OF NOTE? WARS? *WEDDINGS?*

WELL THERE WAS THE *WEDDING*, OF COURSE! HE MARRIED *GUINEVERE*, DIDN'T HE!

IT WAS A BEAUTIFUL DAY. EVEN THE *FAERIE FOLK* CAME TO SEE IT!

HE ALSO MET THE GREAT KNIGHT *LANCELOT.* THEY FOUGHT, AND THEN KING ARTHUR MADE LANCELOT HIS *CHAMPION.*

SO HE FINALLY BECAME THE KING HE *WANTED* TO BE, EH?

AYE, AND *MORE.* KING ARTHUR HAS *UNIFIED THE LANDS*, BROUGHT THE WARRING TRIBES UNDER *ONE RULE.*

FOR THE FIRST TIME IN YEARS WE HAVE *FOOD TO SPARE,* WE FEEL *SAFE* IN OUR HOMES, AND WE KNOW WHAT *HOPE* IS.

ARTHUR SAVED US ALL. ALL OF ALBION *LOVES* HIM.

DOES THAT HELP YOU, MY LORD?

IN A WAY, YES. THANK YOU.

NOW, IF YOU'LL EXCUSE ME – I HAVE A *KING* TO VISIT.

MY KING, I CAN'T EXPLAIN **WHERE** I'VE BEEN.

IT DOESN'T MATTER. YOU'RE HERE NOW.

NO, MY LORD. I MEAN THAT A MATTER OF **HOURS** AGO FOR ME, IT WAS **SEVEN YEARS AGO** FOR YOU!

MORGANA **WON** THE FIGHT AND TRANSPORTED ME HERE.

WELL, THEN YOU HAVE A LOT TO CATCH UP ON!

YOU REMEMBER MY FOSTER FATHER, ECTOR, AND BROTHER, CEI?

IT'S GOOD TO SEE YOU, MERLIN! YOU COULDN'T HAVE TIMED IT BETTER!

WHERE'S LEODEGRANCE AND HIS DAUGHTER?

YOU MEAN MY **WIFE!** GUINEVERE AND I MARRIED **FIVE YEARS AGO!**

SHE'S ATTENDING TO HER FATHER AT CAMELIARD. HE BROKE HIS LEG IN A TOURNEY A COUPLE OF MONTHS AGO.

COME, MERLIN! I HAVE SOMETHING TO SHOW YOU!

OH, ARTHUR. YOU FOUND LOVE –

– BY FORGETTING YOUR **TRUE** LOVE.

MY ADOPTED AUNT WAS *CONCERNED* ABOUT ARTHUR, AND WISHED ME TO ATTEND HIM.

I HAD BEEN TRAINED THROUGHOUT MY LIFE TO BE THE *BEST THAT I COULD BE,* AND VIVIANNE BELIEVED THAT THIS WAS NEEDED BY ARTHUR.

OF *COURSE,* HE DECIDED THAT THE *BEST* WAY TO ATTEND ME WAS TO *CHALLENGE* ME!

FOUR HOURS WE FOUGHT — UNTIL HE SIMPLY STOPPED, KNELT BEFORE ME, AND SWORE TO MY SWORD.

LANCELOT, MY FRIEND, TAKE SOME MEN TO CAMELIARD AND ESCORT THE QUEEN BACK HERE. WE SHALL HAVE A *FEAST!*

YES, MY KING.

REMEMBER TO TAKE *CALIBURN.* YOU ARE THE KING'S CHAMPION AFTER ALL!

LANCELOT HAS ONLY BEEN HERE TWO YEARS, BUT ALREADY HE IS MY CLOSEST FRIEND. AND GUINEVERE'S TOO.

YOU LET HIM TAKE CALIBURN? I THOUGHT THAT ONLY *YOU* — ONLY A MAN *PURE OF HEART AND SOUL* — COULD WIELD IT?

IT'S TRUE, BUT HIS *LINEAGE AND HIS TUTORSHIP* ALLOWS HIM TO WIELD CALIBURN, WHILE PURE OF HEART.

AND I CAN'T SEE *THAT* CHANGING FOR A WHILE. AFTER ALL, THIS IS *CAMELOT....*

"...WHAT COULD *POSSIBLY* CORRUPT HIM HERE?"

AH, THE *MIGHTY* LANCELOT —

— WE'VE BEEN *WAITING* FOR YOU.

WE BRING NEWS FROM YOUR *FAMILY.*

I *HAVE* NO FAMILY IN THE *UNSEELIE COURT.*

AH YES, YOU'VE GONE ALL *SEELIE* ON US, HAVEN'T YOU.

LANCELOT *"OF THE LAKE,"* INDEED.

YOUR ADOPTED FAMILY MIGHT BE ALL *SUNSHINE AND RAINBOWS,* LANCELOT —

— BUT YOUR ORIGIN IS SET IN STONE. *ARCADIAN* STONE.

WATCH CAREFULLY WHAT WORDS YOU SPEAK NEXT, FAE —

— MY PARENTS WERE BOTH MORTAL AND SEELIE. *YOUR* COURT HAS NO SAY HERE.

DO NOT TRY TO *LIE* TO US, KNIGHT. WE KNOW EVERYTHING, EVEN IF *YOU* DON'T.

YOUR MOTHER WAS *UNSEELIE.*

BROUGHT UP BY SEELIE, YET UNSEELIE BY *BIRTH*.

MORTAL MAN STRIVING FOR *GREATNESS*. TRULY A FINE THING TO SEE, EVEN IF IT IS LIKE THE *RABID TALES OF BARDS*.

WE *OFFER* YOU GREATNESS, LANCELOT DU LAC. ON A NICE SILVER PLATE.

I NEED NO GIFT FROM A DARK FAERIE.

IT'S NOT A GIFT, IT'S A *POSITION*.

WE WANT YOU TO BE THE *CHAMPION OF THE DARK FAE*.

YOU WOULD BE OUR *AMBASSADOR* — OUR ENVOY. IT IS A POSITION OF GREAT WEALTH AND POWER.

YOU HAVE A CLOSENESS TO THE KING THAT WE *ENVY*. CLOSENESS WE WISH TO *EXPLOIT*.

YOU COULD DO WHAT YOU LIKED TO ANYONE YOU WANTED. ALL WE WOULD ASK IS YOUR OATH.

ENOUGH!

I ALREADY HAVE A LOYALTY — TO MY *KING*. AND I AM ALREADY *HIS* CHAMPION!

NOW, BE GONE BEFORE I USE *CALIBURN* UPON YOU!

CALIBURN. *SEELIE MAGICK*. ONLY THE PURE OF HEART AND SOUL CAN WIELD IT, BE *HURT* BY IT. HOW LONG DO YOU THINK HE'LL *LET* YOU?

HOW LONG BEFORE HE LEARNS THE *TRUTH* ABOUT YOUR UNSPOKEN LOVE FOR *HIS QUEEN*?

YOU *WILL* FALL, LANCELOT.

AND WHEN YOU DO, WE WILL BE *WAITING* FOR YOU.

WITH *OPEN ARMS*.

SMILE, LANCELOT. MERLIN'S BACK! IT'S A TIME FOR GREAT CHANGE!

I NEVER KNEW MERLIN, *BEDIVERE*, SO I HAVE NO NEED TO BE *CHEERFUL* OF HIS RETURN.

BESIDES, WHEN HE LOOKED AT ME, I FELT A *CHILL* SHIVER DOWN MY SPINE.

HE DOES THAT TO EVERYONE. I REMEMBER A TIME AT STONE HILL—

GAWAIN, *GAWAIN*. YOU MET HIM ONCE. AND YOU WERE *TEN!*

DON'T TRY TO PLAY US LIKE CHILDREN!

HE SAID I HAD A *GREAT FUTURE* AHEAD OF ME.

HE DIDN'T MENTION IT'D INVOLVE *BULL-HEADED IDIOTS* LIKE YOU.

LOOK! WHAT'S THAT?

WHERE? WHAT ARE YOU—

—OH, *NO.*

IT'S LEODEGRANCE. SOMEONE'S TORCHED *CAMELIARD.*

LORD **LEODEGRANCE!** WHAT HAPPENED?

THEY **TOOK** HER! THEY TOOK **GUINEVERE.** SHE'S GONE!

IT WAS **MALEAGANT.** HE HAD AN ARMY OF SOLDIERS!

WE WEREN'T PREPARED. THEY TOOK US APART! THE MAIN FORCE THEN WENT SOUTH –

– BUT MALEAGANT AND SOME MEN TOOK HER **EASTWARD.**

MY REMAINING MEN WENT AFTER THEM, BUT WERE CUT DOWN.

THEY'RE HEADING TOWARD THE **KILLING TREES!**

NO! HE *CAN'T* BE SERIOUS!

WHAT ARE THE KILLING TREES? WHY WOULD HE GO THERE WITHOUT HIS MEN?

IT'S A MESSAGE TO ARTHUR. AND HE *WON'T* BE STAYING THERE LONG.

YEARS AGO, MALEAGANT WAS ULRIC'S *STEWARD.* HE TOOK HIS MASTER'S LOSS PERSONALLY.

ULRIC USED TO TAKE TRAITORS TO THE CROWN TO THE KILLING TREES, WHERE HE WOULD *HANG THEM*

AND THAT'S WHERE MALEAGANT'S TAKEN GUINEVERE. WHAT DO *YOU* THINK HE INTENDS TO DO?

YOU'RE MAKING A BIG MISTAKE HERE. WHEN MY *HUSBAND* HEARS OF THIS —

HE WILL COME FOR US ALL. NO STONE WILL BE UNTURNED. YES, I'VE HEARD IT *ALL* BEFORE.

BUT YOU'LL STILL BE *DEAD*, MY LADY. THE *MESSAGE* WILL BE SENT.

YOUR PRETENDER HUSBAND NEEDS TO BE TAUGHT THAT *SOME* PEOPLE WANT IT BACK THE WAY IT WAS. AND WILL DO *ANYTHING* TO MAKE IT SO.

NOW. BRING HER HERE.

THEY'RE GOING TO *HANG* HER! WE HAVE TO DO SOMETHING!

IT'S TWO-TO-ONE ODDS. ARE WE HAPPY WITH THAT?

TOTALLY.

WHAT THE—

MALEAGANT IS UNFORTUNATELY *DEAD IN A DITCH* IN KENT. BUT WE FELT HIS *APPEARANCE* WAS VITAL.

THE UNSEELIE COURT IS ALL ABOUT THE *STORY*, YOU SEE. *ARTHUR'S* STORY.

I'LL SEE YOU IN *SPRING*, COUSIN.

STRIKE TRUE. BECOME THE *LEGEND*. FOLLOW THE TALE TO THE END.

DIIIIEEEEEEE!!!!

GLAMOUR.

NOTHING BUT *GLAMOUR* AND A *RUSTY BLADE*.

LANCELOT?

CAMELOT.

GUINEVERE! WHAT HAPPENED?

MY FATHER WAS ATTACKED! WE NEED TO SEND AID IMMEDIATELY!

IF IT WASN'T FOR *LANCELOT*...

IF IT WASN'T FOR *ALL* OF US, MY LADY.

MALEAGANT KIDNAPPED THE QUEEN, MY KING. WE TOOK HER BACK.

YOU ARE *TRULY* MY BROTHER! COME, LET ME ARMOR UP! LET US *PUNISH* THE MISCREANT KNIGHT!

THERE IS NO NEED, MY LORD. I *KILLED* HIM.

BUT SIR BEVIS FELL TO AN ARROW.

THEN WE SHALL HOLD A *FEAST* TONIGHT IN HIS HONOR!

AND TO CELEBRATE MY QUEEN'S RETURN — AND MALEAGANT'S DEATH!

MALEAGANT? IT *LOOKED* LIKE HIM, BUT AT THE END I SWEAR I SAW—

IT WAS *MALEAGANT!* NOTHING MORE! JUST A MAN! DO YOU *DOUBT MY WORD?*

NO, IT'S JUST...

THEN THIS CONVERSATION IS *OVER!*

YOU KNOW, YOU SPEND TOO MUCH TIME ALONE. PERHAPS WE SHOULD SORT OUT A *WIFE* FOR YOU.

PERHAPS THE *LADY OF SHALOTT*?

I THINK NOT, MY LORD. THAT DIDN'T END *WELL* THE LAST TIME WE SAW HER.

A-A *WIFE*?

OF COURSE. WHY NOT? I DON'T THINK THAT *WE* SHOULD BE THE ONLY PEOPLE BLISSFULLY HAPPY IN CAMELOT!

WE COULD MAKE IT A *SPRING* WEDDING.

I-I MUST LEAVE THE TABLE. THE FOOD IS TOO RICH FOR MY STOMACH!

WHAT DID I SAY?

CLATTER!

ISN'T IT *ENOUGH* THAT WE SLEEP IN DIFFERENT CHAMBERS? CAN'T SHE EVEN *EAT* WITH ME NOW?

I BELIEVE SHE IS STILL IN SHOCK OVER THE DAY'S EVENTS, MY KING.

LET ME *ATTEND* HER, TO ENSURE THAT SHE IS ALL RIGHT.

OH, ARTHUR. WHAT DID I LEAVE YOU TO?

WHAT DID YOU *BECOME*, THE DAY WE REMOVED YOUR *MEMORIES*?

MY LADY? ARE YOU ALL RIGHT?

YES. IT'S SILLY OF ME, REALLY. TO BE *JEALOUS* OF YOU MARRYING SOMEONE —

— WHILE *I* AM MARRIED TO SOMEONE ELSE.

JUST PROMISE ME THAT *WHEN* YOU MARRY —

— YOU MARRY FOR *LOVE*, OR NOT AT ALL.

GUINEVERE, YOU'RE CRYING!

MY QUEEN — I CAN'T HONOR THAT REQUEST BECAUSE —

— BECAUSE I *ALREADY* LOVE SOMEONE, AND I CAN *NEVER* MARRY HER.

PLEASE, LANCELOT, DON'T SAY ANYTHING ELSE —

— YOUR PURITY IS YOUR *STRENGTH.* TO SAY WHAT YOU THINK—

WOULD BE A *RELIEF.* AND IF SAYING THIS MEANS THAT I AM NO LONGER PURE? THEN SO BE IT.

I LOVE YOU, GUINEVERE. I HAVE, DO NOW, AND ALWAYS WILL.

LANCELOT, I'VE BEEN SO LONELY . . .

LOOK AT HIM. PLUMMETING HAPPILY TO HIS DOOM. *DAMNING* CAMELOT AND HIS KING WITH A *KISS*.

IS *THIS* WHY YOU BROUGHT ME BACK TO ALBION, MORGANA? TRICKS AND LIES?

IS *THIS* WHY I STAND IN A FAERIE REALM, *STILL NOT KING*?

SHUT UP, *ULRIC*. YOUR DAYS AS KING ARE OVER, BUT YOU STILL HAVE A *PART* TO PLAY.

ARROGANT WITCH! I SHOULD HAVE TAUGHT YOU MANNERS WHEN I—

I WAS TAUGHT "MANNERS" BY A FORCE *FAR WORSE* THAN YOU, STEPFATHER.

NOW. YOU CAN EITHER TAKE YOUR PLACE AT MY SIDE, OR I CAN *KILL YOU* WHERE YOU STAND.

ACK— I—*ALL RIGHT!*

— GASP —

SO WHAT'S NEXT? WE PLAY WITH THE PRETTY BOY KNIGHT SOME MORE?

NO, THAT'S TOO SIMPLE, TOO FAST.

I WANT TO HURT ARTHUR ON A *LONG-TERM* BASIS.

IT'S TIME FOR ARTHUR TO HAVE A MIDNIGHT VISITOR. HIS *TRUE* LOVE.

IT'S TIME FOR *FAERIE GLAMOUR* TO COME OUT AND PLAY.

ARTHUR'S CHAMBERS.

HRR —
NO...

WHA —
WHO'S
THAT?

GUINEVERE?
IS THAT
YOU?

IT IS I,
ARTHUR.

YOUR *TRUE*
LOVE.

VIVIANNE?
WHAT ARE YOU —
NO, *STOP* —
GET OFF —

WHY DO
YOU STOP ME?
YOU *LOVE* ME.
YOU *WANT* ME. YOU
CREATED THIS
GLAMOUR
OF ME.

ACCEPT
ME. TAKE ME
IN YOUR
ARMS.

LOVE
ME.

PERFECT. WE HAVE HIM *EXACTLY* WHERE WE NEED HIM NOW.

IS THAT — MY GOD! THAT'S A *BABY*?

YOU'VE STOLEN A BABY FROM ARTHUR?

DON'T BE A FOOL. I'VE DONE MUCH *MORE* THAN THAT.

I HAVE STOLEN SOME OF THE *VERY ESSENCE* OF ARTHUR — HIS VERY BEING.

AND FROM IT I HAVE SHAPED THIS CHILD — A *DUPLICATE* OF ARTHUR IN EVERY WAY.

TAKEN FROM ARTHUR TO *BE* ARTHUR. *OUR* ARTHUR.

YOU BROUGHT ME HERE TO *BABYSIT?*

NOT QUITE. HERE IN *ARCADIA* TIME MOVES DIFFERENTLY THAN IN OUR WORLD.

REMEMBER WHEN ARTHUR AGED TWO YEARS IN A *DAY?* WELL, THIS IS SIMILAR.

IN BUT MONTHS, THIS CHILD WILL HAVE AGED *TWO DECADES* IN ARCADIA.

TWO DECADES OF SOLID TUTORING FROM BOTH OF US. A RIVAL TO ARTHUR. HIS . . . *SON,* I SUPPOSE.

A SON TO RAIN MORE *PAIN,* MORE *SUFFERING,* AND MORE *DREAD* ON THE PEOPLE THAN EVER BEFORE.

HEH. *MORE DREAD.* I LIKE THAT.

FOR TEN YEARS I *SUFFERED* BECAUSE ARTHUR WAS TOO *IMPORTANT,* TOO *SPECIAL.* BUT NOW ARTHUR *WILL* SUFFER FOR ME.

MY CREATION WILL KILL ARTHUR AND *BECOME* ARTHUR. AND WE *WILL* CONTROL HIM.

FINALLY I SHALL BE ALBION'S ONCE AND FUTURE *QUEEN.*

AND THEN THEY DISCOVER THAT SHE'S ONLY A *HAG* DURING THE DAY!

I STILL THINK IT NEEDS MORE WORK, *TALLIESIN.*

HELP... ME...

PLEASE... MERLIN...

ARTHUR!

QUICK! *GET MERLIN!*

THUD!

STAY WITH ME, ARTHUR! WHO DID THIS?

WHO DID THIS?

HOW ARE YOU FEELING TODAY, MY KING?

BETTER. STRONGER. NOT AS STRONG AS I WAS—

—BUT SLOWLY, DAY BY DAY, I GET THERE.

THE EMISSARY FROM *AVALON* RETURNED. BRAN STILL WON'T ACCEPT YOUR APOLOGY.

AND APPARENTLY *THE GREEN KNIGHT* HAS GONE MISSING.

I DON'T BLAME HIM. I WOULDN'T HAVE, EITHER. IT WAS JUST—WELL, VIVIANNE—

—IT WAS *HER*, MERLIN. SHE FELT SO *REAL*.

FOR YEARS I'VE FELT *HOLLOW*, AS IF *MISSING* SOMETHING. I THOUGHT IT WAS THE LOSS OF YOU, BUT WHEN YOU RETURNED IT WAS STILL THERE.

AND WHEN VIVIANNE—OR WHATEVER IT WAS—APPEARED, SUDDENLY I WAS *COMPLETE*. AND THEN IT WAS GONE AGAIN.

IT'S ALMOST LIKE I *LOST* SOMETHING, BUT DON'T REMEMBER WHAT IT WAS.

A VEIL HAS BEEN PULLED TO THE SIDE. I *LOVE* GUINEVERE, BUT THERE WAS *SOMEONE ELSE*, WASN'T THERE? SOMEONE I'VE FORGOTTEN?

THERE WAS, AND IT *WAS* VIVIANNE. YOU FELL IN LOVE IN AVALON.

BUT YOU KNEW THAT TO *RULE* ALBION, YOU WOULD EVENTUALLY HAVE TO MARRY *ANOTHER*, AND SO YOU BEGGED ME TO REMOVE YOUR *MEMORIES* OF HER.

SHE BECAME NOTHING MORE THAN A STRAY THOUGHT.

I—I THINK I REMEMBER. THIS HAPPENED THE NIGHT YOU LEFT!

BUT WHY DO YOU TELL ME *NOW?*

BECAUSE YOU CHOSE THIS PATH, AND ONLY *YOU* CAN REMOVE THIS CURSE YOU LAID ON YOURSELF.

AND I TELL YOU NOW BECAUSE YOU WON'T *REMEMBER*, ARTHUR. BY THE TIME THIS CONVERSATION ENDS, YOU'LL HAVE *FORGOTTEN* AGAIN.

THAT'S HOW THE CURSE WORKS, YOU SEE.

BUT WHAT IF I DON'T *WANT* TO FORGET?

GOD HELP ME, I WAS IN LOVE WITH THE *LADY OF THE LAKE?* HOW DO I EXPLAIN THIS TO *GUINEVERE?*

ARTHUR, I THINK YOU'LL HAVE *MORE* TO WORRY ABOUT IN YOUR MARRIAGE THAN *FORGOTTEN LOVE.*

BY THE TIME YOU *REMEMBER* EVERYTHING, YOUR MARRIAGE WILL HAVE BEEN BROKEN BY LANCELOT AND GUINEVERE'S *BETRAYAL,* ANYWAY.

LANCELOT AND *GUINEVERE?* ARE YOU SURE?

ABSOLUTELY. BUT DON'T WORRY. YOU'LL FORGET *ALL ABOUT THIS* IN A MOMENT.

WHAT WERE WE TALKING ABOUT?

NOTHING, MY KING. NOTHING AT ALL.

WHERE ON *EARTH* ARE GUINEVERE AND LANCELOT?

I SENT HIM TO FIND HER OVER *HALF AN HOUR* AGO!

I'VE NO IDEA, ARTHUR. PERHAPS HE GOT LOST?

DOUBTFUL. THE AMOUNT OF TIMES HE'S ESCORTED HER TO HER QUARTERS, HE'D KNOW THE ROUTE BETTER THAN TO HIS OWN.

PERHAPS I SHOULD—

ARTHUR!

CRASH

ARTHUR PENDRAGON! THE BOY WHO BECAME KING!

THE *LIAR* MORE LIKELY! THE STEALER AND *DESTROYER* OF HEARTS!

SIR BERTILAK, I HAVE BEEN WORRIED ABOUT YOU.

I HEARD THAT YOU HAD GONE MISSING FROM AVALON.

I CARE NOT ABOUT YOUR *WORRY!* I DEMAND RECOMPENSE FOR THE LADY OF THE LAKE'S *HONOR!*

HONOR THAT *YOU* DEFILED!

ARTHUR DIDN'T DEFILE VIVIANNE! *SHE* WAS THE ONE WHO CAME TO HIS BED!

NO, CEI, THAT WAS A CREATURE OF *GLAMOUR,* MADE TO LOOK LIKE HER.

SHE IS A *WRONGED PARTY,* AND BERTILAK HAS A *RIGHT* TO JUSTICE.

WHAT DO YOU WANT, BERTILAK? WHAT DOES *VIVIANNE* WANT?

FOR HOW ARTHUR *TREATED* HER WHEN SHE OFFERED HIM A *CURE,* I WANT HIS *HEAD,* MERLIN.

SHE WANTS NOTHING. SHE KNOWS IT WAS AN UNSEELIE GAME. BUT THAT IS *NOT THE POINT!*

I SEE YOU'RE STILL NOT WELL ENOUGH TO *FIGHT.* AND YOUR *CHAMPION* SEEMS TO BE MISSING.

SO INSTEAD, I CHALLENGE YOU TO A *CONTEST.*

VERY WELL.

NO, MY LORD, YOU **WILL NOT** PLAY THESE FAERIE GAMES!

IF SOMEONE NEEDS TO BE THE GREEN KNIGHT'S **PLAYTHING**, THEN IT SHALL BE ME!

TELL ME THE RULES, SIR BERTILAK. WHAT GAME DO WE PLAY?

IT IS A SIMPLE ONE, SIR GAWAIN. EVEN **YOU** CAN PLAY THIS ONE.

YOU JUST HAVE TO **CUT OFF** MY HEAD.

IF I SURVIVE, I CUT YOURS OFF IN A **YEAR AND A DAY.** A FINE LENGTH OF TIME. IN FACT, THE **SAME** AGREEMENT ARTHUR MADE IN **AVALON.**

YOU'RE **INSANE!** YOU WON'T SURVIVE! AT THIS RANGE I CAN'T MISS!

THEN IT WILL PROVE THAT ARTHUR IS **JUST** IN HIS ACTIONS, AND HONOR WILL BE RETURNED.

STRIKE, KNIGHT. OR ARE YOU TOO **SCARED?**

NEVER.

SHUNK!

CLATTER!

A FINE BLOW, SIR GAWAIN.

BUT IT LOOKS LIKE *MY* CAUSE IS *TRUE*, DOESN'T IT?

IN A *YEAR AND A DAY*, ARTHUR, I WILL RETURN AND TAKE MY SWING AT SIR GAWAIN'S HEAD, AS HE TOOK YOUR PLACE.

IF THE AX FALLS AND *DOESN'T* CUT HIS HEAD OFF? THEN I WILL AGREE THAT MY LADY'S *HONOR* IS RETURNED. IF NOT –

– JUST REMEMBER THAT WHATEVER HAPPENS, IT IS *YOUR FAULT*, KING ARTHUR.

EVERY LAST PIECE OF IT.

SEE YOU IN A *YEAR AND A DAY*, MORTAL.

ARE YOU ALL RIGHT?

BLOODY *FAERIE GAMES!* THAT'S ALL THIS WAS!

HOW DO I RETURN THE FAVOR IN A YEAR? MY HEAD WON'T DO WHAT *HIS* DID!

WELL, THE *BAD* NEWS IS THAT A YEAR FOR BERTILAK IS ONLY A DAY FOR YOU—

—SO EXPECT HIM BACK AFTER DAWN TOMORROW.

THE *GOOD* NEWS IS THAT IT'LL ALL BE OVER SOON, THOUGH!

FAERIES! LANCELOT SHOULD HAVE BEEN HERE FOR THIS! THIS WAS *HIS* FIGHT, NOT MINE!

I'M SO GLAD TO SEE THAT YOU FIND THIS *FUNNY,* WIZARD!

OH, COME ON, ARTHUR— BERTILAK WON'T CUT OFF GAWAIN'S HEAD.

HE WANTS TO CUT OFF *YOURS.*

IT'S JUST A SHAME YOUR *CHAMPION* WASN'T HERE. I WONDER WHERE HE IS?

YOU AND ME BOTH. WHEREVER HE IS . . .

"...HE'D BETTER HAVE A **DAMNED GOOD REASON** FOR HIS DELAY!"

WE'RE SO **LATE!** THEY'LL BE WAITING FOR US!

IT'S A **ROYAL FEAST.** WITH THE AMOUNT OF PEOPLE IN THE HALL, THEY WON'T EVEN HAVE NOTICED THAT WE AREN'T THERE.

OF COURSE, I MIGHT BE **WRONG.**

HO, GAWAIN! WE WERE JUST COMING!

I'VE BEEN **LOOKING** FOR YOU, **CHAMPION.** YOU'RE WANTED AT COURT.

BUT I SHOULD HAVE GUESSED YOU'D BE **PICKING FLOWERS** — WITH **HER.**

THAT **"HER"** IS THE QUEEN OF —

I DON'T WANT TO HEAR WHAT YOU HAVE TO **SAY,** LANCELOT!

YOUR KING **NEEDED** YOU, **AND YOU WEREN'T** THERE!

ARTHUR IS IN TROUBLE?

WAS. LUCKILY HE STILL HAD A COUPLE OF LOYAL KNIGHTS WHO KNEW WHAT THEIR **PRIORITIES** WERE.

I TOOK AN **AX-SWING** FOR YOU TODAY.

YOU CAN TAKE THE **NEXT** ONE.

EITHER OF YOU. I DON'T CARE ANY MORE.

I FOUND YOUR MISSING CHAMPION, MY LORD.

MY KING, I AM *SORRY* FOR OUR DELAY.

THE QUEEN WAS FEELING UNWELL AND I HAD TO WAIT FOR HER. BUT GAWAIN'S WORDS—

THE FEAST HAS *ENDED*, MY QUEEN. WHICH MEANS THAT YOU'RE NOT LATE—YOU WERE *ABSENT ENTIRELY*.

AND IF *EITHER* OF YOU HAVE AN ISSUE WITH GAWAIN, WHO TOOK LANCELOT'S PLACE TONIGHT IN MY *DEFENSE*—

—THEN YOU SPEAK TO *HIM*. WORK OUT YOUR ISSUES.

I'LL DO BETTER THAN THAT, MY KING! I *CHALLENGE* LANCELOT!

I'VE HAD *ENOUGH* OF THEIR LIES! *LANCELOT* AND *HIS QUEEN LOVER!* DO YOU THINK WE HADN'T *NOTICED?*

I SAW YOU AT THE *CARAVAN!* WE'VE SEEN YOU IN THE *GARDEN!*

THERE'S NOT A *KNIGHT IN CAMELOT* WHO DOESN'T KNOW OF YOUR SECRET! YOU MAKE A *MOCKERY* OF THE MARRIAGE—

OH, TRUST ME, GAWAIN, *THAT* ISN'T A MOCKERY OF THEIR MARRIAGE—

—BUT I'M ABOUT TO SHOW YOU SOMETHING THAT *IS*.

HELLO, *BROTHER*.

TODAY WE SETTLE AN ARGUMENT BETWEEN TWO OF ARTHUR'S FINEST KNIGHTS: *GAWAIN* AND *LANCELOT*.

GAWAIN ACCUSES LANCELOT OF *ADULTERY*, OF FALLING FROM GRACE. AND LANCELOT *DENIES* THESE CLAIMS.

THEY HAVE DECIDED ON *TRIAL BY COMBAT* TO PROVE WHOSE WORD IS TRUE.

IF THIS FIGHT ENDS AND YOU ARE PROVEN A *LIAR?* FOR WHAT YOU HAVE SAID ABOUT MY DAUGHTER—

—I WILL *CUT OUT YOUR SPLEEN* WITH A CUTLERY KNIFE.

AND YOU— IF YOU PROVE TO BE A *FALSE* KNIGHT—

—I'LL LEAVE YOU TO *ARTHUR*. AND IT'LL BE *WORSE*.

FIGHT!

I DON'T WANT TO *FIGHT* YOU, GAWAIN. YOU'RE MY BROTHER KNIGHT—

I'M NO BROTHER TO *ADULTEROUS SCUM* LIKE YOU! YOU'VE BROKEN THE CIRCLE! *DOOMED US ALL!*

AND THAT HARLOT IS NO *QUEEN OF MINE!*

NEVER CALL GUINEVERE THAT!

"I AM NO LONGER PURE OF HEART, MY LORD!"

"BUT GUINEVERE IS *BLAMELESS* IN THIS! IT WAS MY *FAULT*! *SPARE HER*!"

"IT WAS *TRUE*? YOU AND *LANCELOT*?"

"I *LOVE* HIM, ARTHUR— A LOVE THAT *WE* NEVER FOUND."

"BUT A *LOVE* YOU SEEMED TO FIND FOR *VIVIANNE*!"

"COME ON, WART. LET'S GET YOU OUT OF HERE BEFORE SOMETHING *STUPID* HAPPENS, EH?"

"*VIVIANNE*? I DON'T EVEN REMEMBER WHAT SHE *LOOKS* LIKE."

"THAT IS, I SEEM TO RECALL . . ."

"WHY DIDN'T YOU *TELL* ME OF THIS? YOU COULD HAVE *TOLD ME* OF THIS!"

"WE WERE *MORE* THAN MAN AND WIFE; WE WERE *BEST FRIENDS*!"

"I WANTED TO, BUT I WAS TOO *SCARED*! IT WAS SO *WRONG*—"

"—YET AT THE SAME TIME FELT *SO RIGHT*!"

"ARGH! MY HEAD— *SPLITTING*!"

"ARTHUR! ARE YOU ALL RIGHT?"

"SPEAK TO ME! *WHAT'S HAPPENING*?"

"ARTHUR!"

"I—I REMEMBER IT ALL. . . ."

I BEGGED YOU? TO FORGET *VIVIANNE?* TO FORGET *THIS?*

AND YOU *LET* ME? YOU AGREED FOR ME TO WALK *BLINDLY INTO BETRAYAL?* THEN WHY *NOW* REMIND ME?

I DIDN'T. YOUR SUBCONSCIOUS DID, BECAUSE YOU *NEEDED* TO REMEMBER. YOU NEEDED TO REMEMBER THAT GUINEVERE *WASN'T* YOUR FIRST LOVE. THAT YOU TOO LOVED *ANOTHER* AS SHE DOES.

AND YOU NEEDED TO REMEMBER FOR *HIM.*

IT HAS BEEN A *YEAR AND A DAY* IN AVALON, SIR GAWAIN.

ARE YOU READY TO UPHOLD *YOUR END* OF THE BARGAIN?

SIR BERTILAK. I DIDN'T *KNOW* ABOUT THE GLAMOUR! HE THOUGHT I WAS UNCARING AND RUDE TO VIVIANNE!

AND IT WAS *TRUE!* BUT GAWAIN CANNOT DIE FOR *MY* SINS!

I WILL **HONOR** OUR BARGAIN, SIR KNIGHT.

ALTHOUGH IT GIVES ME NO **PLEASURE** TO DIE THIS DAY.

I HAVE TO **STOP** THIS!

ARTHUR, **PLEASE!**

TO TAKE ON THE GREEN KNIGHT IS **SUICIDE!** AS MERLIN SAID, HE **WON'T KILL GAWAIN!**

AND WHAT IF HE **DOES?** WILL YOU GIVE ME ONE **MORE** REASON TO HATE LANCELOT, GUINEVERE? FOR **HE** SHOULD BE STANDING THERE! MY **CHAMPION!**

GAWAIN, YOU HAVE **DONE** YOUR PART. AND I HAVE DONE **MINE.**

LET ME AT LEAST **DIE** IN YOUR PLACE, TO DO THE ONE THING THAT I **SHOULD** HAVE DONE TODAY.

DON'T BE A **FOOL,** LANCELOT! GET ON YOUR HORSE AND **RIDE!**

ESCAPE! BEFORE ARTHUR **STOPS** YOU!

STRIKE **ME,** COUSIN. FOR I WAS CAMELOT'S CHAMPION THE NIGHT YOU ARRIVED, AND AS SUCH SHOULD HAVE BEEN THE ONE TO **STRIKE** THE BLOW.

BUT **I** STRUCK THE BLOW, GREEN KNIGHT! SO **STRIKE ME!**

SHUNK!

WHERE ONCE I SAW A **BOY**, NOW I SEE A MAN.

YOU HAVE REGAINED YOUR LOST MEMORIES, AND YOUR DEBT IS FULFILLED.

YOU ARE THE **TRUE** KING ONCE MORE.

GATHER THE **SHARDS OF THE BLADE**. WE NEED TO RETURN IT TO ITS RIGHTFUL KEEPER.

MY LORD, YOU **CANNOT**! LET ME DO IT FOR YOU! YOUR CHAMPION IS NO MORE.

WHO BETTER THAN **ONE OF YOUR KNIGHTS**?

TOO LONG HAVE I LET **OTHERS** FIGHT MY BATTLES, GAWAIN. IT IS TIME TO FACE MY FOES IN PERSON.

AND YOU HAVE TAKEN MY PLACE **TOO MANY** TIMES ALREADY, MY FRIEND. IT IS TIME FOR YOU TO REST.

GUINEVERE, WE BOTH LOVE **OTHERS**. BUT WHILE I MADE MYSELF FORGET, YOU WERE FORCED TO **LIVE** WITH YOUR SECRET.

LANCELOT, I CANNOT HATE YOU FOR FOLLOWING WHERE **FATE** LED YOU, AS I MUST FOLLOW MYSELF. SO GO IN PEACE.

HEAR THIS! NOBODY SHALL TOUCH GUINEVERE OR LANCELOT! THEY ARE **BANISHED FROM CAMELOT** —

— BUT STILL **WELCOME IN ALBION**!

A GOOD CHOICE, ARTHUR.

FOR WE HAVE **PLANS** FOR LANCELOT.

AS THE LADY OF THE LAKE, *ALL* LAKES ARE YOUR PORTALS, VIVIANNE.

AND THEREFORE *ALL* LAKES WILL PASS THE *MESSAGE* I MUST GIVE TO YOU.

I'M—

—I'M *SORRY*.

I *LOVE* YOU. I ALWAYS HAVE. BUT FOR A TIME I NEEDED TO *FORGET* THIS.

BUT INSTEAD OF FORGETTING THE *LOVE* I HAD FOR YOU, I FORGOT *YOU* ENTIRELY.

IN THE END, MORGANA TRICKED ME. SHE SENT MY *GREATEST LOVE* TO SEDUCE ME SO THAT SHE COULD CREATE A COPY OF ME—

—SO THAT SHE COULD CREATE *MORDRED*.

AT FIRST I DIDN'T UNDERSTAND WHY I SAW *YOU* THAT NIGHT, AND I STRUCK OUT. AT YOU, AT MY FRIENDS...

CALIBURN WAS DESTROYED BECAUSE OF MY STUPIDITY. MY FEARS. MY *COWARDICE*.

ALBION NO LONGER HAS A CHAMPION *WORTHY* ENOUGH TO WIELD THE BLADE. AND THEREFORE...

...I RETURN CALIBURN TO YOU!

SPLASH!

ALL I HOPE IS THAT ONE DAY YOU CAN *FORGIVE* ME. THAT ONE DAY WE CAN PERHAPS BECOME *FRIENDS* AGAIN.

I KNOW WE CAN NEVER RETURN TO WHAT WE ONCE HAD. I KNOW THIS IS MY *FAULT.* AND IT WILL HAUNT ME FOREVER.

SWWOOSSSHHH

WHAT THE—

THAT'S A SHARD OF *CALIBURN?* THEN IT CAN'T BE USED!

ONLY THE PURE OF HEART OR *ARTHUR* CAN USE THE BLADE!

YOU FORGET ONE SMALL THING IN THE *FIFTEEN YEARS* YOU'VE TRAINED MORDRED, ULRIC —

— AND THAT IS THAT HE *IS* ARTHUR. IN EVERY MINUTE DETAIL. *OUR* ARTHUR.

IN TEN MORE YEARS HE WILL BE *READY.* AND IN ALBION ONLY *WEEKS* WILL HAVE PASSED.

ARTHUR IS WEAK. CONFUSED. *BROKEN.* AND WE WILL USE THIS TO DEFEAT HIM IN BATTLE.

BUT EVEN WITH A MAGIC SPEAR, I NEED AN *ARMY,* MOTHER.

WHERE WILL WE FIND THAT? FROM THE UNSEELIE COURT?

FROM THE *NORTHLANDS,* MY SON. HIRED HELP FROM THE FROZEN WASTES.

THE *SAXONS* WILL AID US. THEY OWE ULRIC A DEBT.

ARTHUR'S PEOPLE ARE LOST, FRACTURED. AND THEY WILL LOOK TO A *NEW* LEADER. A *BETTER, PURER* ARTHUR.

AND WITH YOUR MAGICAL SPEAR, *RHONGOMIANT,* YOU WILL *CLAIM* YOUR BIRTHRIGHT.

KILL ARTHUR. *REPLACE* ARTHUR.

BE ARTHUR.

CAMELOT.

WHAT DO I *DO*, MERLIN? HOW DO I *DEFEAT* MORGANA?

I THINK WE BOTH KNOW THAT THIS IS A BATTLE WE WON'T WALK AWAY FROM *ALIVE*, MY KING.

BUT NO MATTER WHAT, WE *MUST* STOP MORGANA AND THE UNSEELIE COURT.

THE REPORTS SAY THAT *SAXONS* ARE INVADING — THAT THEY HEAD FOR CAMELOT. IS THIS THE START?

IS THIS HOW IT ALL *ENDS*?

DEAR ECTOR, I DID INDEED.

I RELEASE YOU ALL FROM YOUR *OATHS* TO ME.

WHAT?

I HAVE SPENT MY LIFE SEEING VISIONS OF MY *FUTURE*, AND THERE IS ONLY ONE SCENE I SEE. MY *DEATH*.

IT APPROACHES, AND I HAVE NO DESIRE TO CAUSE *YOUR* DEATHS IN THE PROCESS. SO TAKE MY LOVE AND LEAVE CAMELOT. BE *SAFE*.

IF YOU DECIDE TO STAY — TO STAND *WITH* ME — THEN DRINK WITH ME FROM THIS MOST *HOLY OF GRAILS*, THE *CHALICE* GIVEN TO ME BY THE SEELIE COURT IN MY DARKEST HOUR.

BECOME MY BROTHERS *ONCE MORE* IN THIS MOST SOLEMN PACT.

I'VE LOOKED AFTER YOU ALL MY LIFE, WART. NO REASON TO STOP NOW.

UNTIL THE *VERY END*.

YOU'RE MY *SON*, ARTHUR — MORE SO THAN UTHER'S. I RAISED YOU.

AND I'LL BE DAMNED IF I *DESERT* YOU NOW. UNTIL THE END IT IS.

I DON'T *UNDERSTAND*, LANCELOT! WHY DO YOU HAVE TO DO THIS?

WHY DO YOU HAVE TO *LEAVE* ME?

BECAUSE THIS IS HOW IT HAS *TO BE*.

BECAUSE THIS IS HOW *MY STORY ENDS*.

COME, MY PRINCE.

THE *UNSEELIE COURT* HAS NEED OF THEIR NEW *CHAMPION*.

I'M *SORRY*, MY LOVE.

APOLOGIZE TO ARTHUR FOR ME.

WONDERFUL! THE CHAMPION *FALLS*!

THE UNSEELIE COURT CANNOT *FAIL*!

I TOLD YOU THIS WOULD *WORK*!

NOW, LET US *END* THIS CHARADE!

WHAT OF YOU, *OTTA BIG-KNIFE*?

WILL YOUR SAXON SOLDIERS *FIGHT* FOR ME? WILL THEY FIGHT FOR *MORDRED*?

WHILE I LEAD THEM, MY SOLDIERS WILL FIGHT FOR *GOLD*. AND IF *YOU* ARE THE ONE GIVING US THIS GOLD — THEN WE WILL *FIGHT* FOR YOU.

HOW LONG HAVE YOU BEEN ABLE TO SPY INTO THE UNSEELIE REALM, SIR BERTILAK? MORE *FAERIE MAGICK*?

WE HAVE SOMEONE *HIDDEN* IN THE COURT. THEY ALLOW US ENTRY PAST THE *WARDINGS*. AND WHILE MORGANA PLOTS, SHE PAYS LITTLE ATTENTION.

SHE IS PREPARING HER MAGICIANS AND HER SOLDIERS FOR WAR, BUT THEY WILL BE *ARROGANT* AND *UNDISCIPLINED*.

ULRIC HAS SCANT TIME TO TRAIN THESE MERCENARIES TO HIS STYLE OF FIGHTING. IF WE STRIKE THEM *HARD*, THEY WILL FLEE.

IT WILL BE A BLOODY BATTLE, ARTHUR. AND IT WILL BEGIN SOON. *BE READY*.

WHAT MANNER OF **MADNESS** IS THIS?

WHO COMES?

CALM, OLD FRIEND. MY MOTHER INFORMED ME OF THIS.

HE IS AN EMISSARY OF THE **UNSEELIE COURT.** HE IS AN ALLY.

MY PRINCE **MORDRED.** MY KING **ULRIC.**

GREETINGS FROM THE UNSEELIE COURT.

UNSEELIE COURT BE **DAMNED!** WHO THE BLAZES **ARE** YOU? TAKE OFF THAT HELMET!

APOLOGIES, MY KING.

NO! IT **CANNOT BE!**

I AM **LANCELOT DU LAC.** I AM THE **DARK CHAMPION** OF THE **UNSEELIE COURT.**

AND I AM HERE TO **KILL ARTHUR** FOR YOU.

THEY HAVE **NUMBERS,** BUT WE HAVE BETTER TACTICIANS. ECTOR AND BEDIVERE WILL—

WHAT'S GOING ON?

GOOD **MORNING,** MY KING.

I'VE COME TO **HELP** YOU AGAINST THE USURPER TO YOUR THRONE. I HOPE THAT'S ALL RIGHT?

GUINEVERE! WHAT ARE YOU **DOING!**

YOU BANISHED ME FROM CAMELOT, BUT NOT **ALBION.** AND SO I **FIGHT** FOR IT.

AS FOR LANCELOT, HE FIGHTS FOR **MORDRED.** THE UNSEELIE COURT MADE HIM THEIR CHAMPION.

SO IT'S TRUE. LANCELOT REALLY **DOES** BECOME MY ENEMY.

YES, MY KING. . . .

". . . LANCELOT IS A **HERO** NO LONGER."

A MESSAGE FROM YOUR **MOTHER**, MY LORD. WE HAVE NEWS FROM OUR **SPIES** IN ARTHUR'S BATTLE LINE.

THE QUEEN **GUINEVERE** HAS ARRIVED – AND HAS INFORMED ARTHUR THAT LANCELOT HAS TURNED **TRAITOR** TO HIS KING.

SO HE **REALLY HAS** TURNED UNSEELIE THEN? EXCELLENT!

ALL THE SWEETER A BLOW WHEN IT COMES FROM A ONE-TIME **BROTHER**, EH, ULRIC?

I **STILL** DON'T TRUST HIM. TO BE CORRUPTED **THAT QUICKLY** BY THE UNSEELIE COURT . . .

WHAT, LIKE **YOU**? WHEN YOU **RAMMED A KNIFE INTO UTHER'S BACK**?

LANCELOT **STAYS**. HE FIGHTS WITH US.

I HAVE ONE REQUEST, MY LORDS. LET ME STRIKE THE **FIRST BLOW** OF THE BATTLE.

LET ME KILL THE KING AS IF CUTTING THE HEAD OFF A **SNAKE**.

ONE BLOW TO END THE WAR? **AMBITIOUS!** I LIKE IT!

VERY WELL. DRAW YOUR SWORD. **YOU** WILL START OUR BATTLE. AND **YOU** WILL STRIKE THE FIRST BLOW.

THANK YOU, MY PRINCE.

FOR ARTHUR!

SHUNK!

OF COURSE IT HAD TO... END LIKE THIS.

I FIND REDEMPTION NO...OTHER WAY, MY LOVE.

BUT I LOVE YOU! I CAN'T LOSE YOU!

THEY THOUGHT THEY HAD ME... BUT I... TRICKED THEM.

I HAVE ALWAYS... BEEN YOUR SERVANT... MY KING. BUT NOW FAERIE SPRING CALLS....

GET TO YOUR HORSES. WE END THIS NOW.

TAKE LANCELOT'S BODY TO CAMELOT. ARRANGE IT IN STATE.

WHAT OF ME, ARTHUR? I HAVE NOTHING.

GIVE GUINEVERE AN HONOR GUARD. SHE'LL FIGHT WITH US TODAY.

AND THOSE WHO SAY SHE ISN'T WORTHY ANSWER TO ME. GUINEVERE IS CAMELOT'S QUEEN, AS LANCELOT WAS ITS CHAMPION.

CAMELOT'S CHAMPION TO THE VERY END.

LET US FOLLOW HIS EXAMPLE.

DIIIEEEEE!!!!

FOR LANCELOT!

SHUNK!

- GACK -

THANK YOU, GAWAIN!

MY LADY, MY QUEEN. I'M SORRY FOR THE THINGS THAT I SAID.

STOP BEING SO SOFT — AND FIGHT SOME SAXONS WITH ME.

ARCADIA.

IS THIS THE **BEST** THAT YOU CAN DO?

FOR THE — NNG — **MOMENT!**

I HAVE THE POWER OF THE **UNSEELIE COURT** RUNNING THROUGH MY VEINS! YOU'RE JUST A MAN!

A MAN I **DEFEATED WITH EASE** LAST TIME!

REALLY? THEN WHY ARE YOU FINDING IT SO HARD TO DO THE JOB **THIS** TIME? AND HOW DID I GET INTO YOUR **CHAMBERS?**

BECAUSE YOU'RE **WRONG,** MORGANA. THE UNSEELIE COURT HAVE **LEFT YOU** DRY.

WITH A **CHAMPION,** AND A **BATTLE** TO FIGHT, THEY'VE TAKEN THEIR POWER FOR THEMSELVES.

ALL YOU DO IS DRAIN THE **DARK GLAMOUR** THAT HAS CONTROLLED YOU ALL THESE YEARS.

YOU **LIE!** THEY WOULDN'T **FORSAKE ME!**

OF **COURSE** THEY WOULD. YOU WERE NEVER ONE OF THEM. THEY WANTED **ARTHUR.**

I **MADE** YOU LIKE THIS. **ALL** OF THIS — THE WAR, THE DEATHS — IS **ALL MY FAULT.**

AND I MUST MAKE **AMENDS** FOR THAT. I FORGIVE **YOU,** BUT PLEASE FORGIVE **ME.**

WHAT ARE YOU DOING? **NOO!!**

– KAFF –

MERLIN! WHAT HAPPENED?

I *BURNED AWAY* MORGANA'S UNSEELIE TAINT, NIMUE.

WITH IT GONE, SHE'S AS SHE WAS. AND WE WERE *EVICTED* FROM THE UNSEELIE REALM.

WIZARD, I CAN THINK *CLEARLY* FOR THE FIRST TIME IN – HNF – *YEARS.*

I REGRET – KAFF – SO MUCH. BUT I . . . FORGIVE YOU . . . .

COME ON! THESE ARE JUST *BURNS!* WE CAN HEAL THESE!

I AM SO SORRY, MY LOVE, BUT *NOTHING* CAN – HNG – HEAL *THESE* WOUNDS.

I USED MY *LIFE'S ENERGY* TO BURN THE GLAMOUR AWAY. I'M *DYING.*

YOU CAN'T DIE. I WON'T *LET* YOU.

I'M A *DRYAD* – A TREE SPRITE. I CAN PROTECT YOU, *HOLD* YOU, GIVE YOU THE TIME NEEDED TO GAIN YOUR STRENGTH.

LITTLE BY LITTLE, NO MATTER HOW MANY YEARS, OR EVEN *CENTURIES* IT TAKES TO HEAL YOU.

I *LOVE* YOU, MERLIN AMBROSIUS. NOW *KISS* ME.

HE'S GONE.

WE NEED TO START LOOKING FOR SURVIVORS.

IGNORE WHAT HE SAID. *YOU* MUST DECIDE WHICH OF YOU *RULES* NOW THAT HE IS GONE.

NO, MY QUEEN. ARTHUR SPOKE THE *TRUTH.* WE SAW YOU IN BATTLE TODAY.

YOU FOUGHT WITH US. YOU *BLED* WITH US. UNTIL CAMELOT FALLS, UNTIL THE VERY END . . .

. . . WE PLEDGE OUR LIVES TO YOU.

AND YOU CAN *ALL* STOP THAT *RIGHT NOW.*

YOU CAN SWEAR ALL THE OATHS AND PROMISES YOU WANT TO — *LATER.* BUT FIRST WE HAVE ONE LAST PROMISE TO KEEP.

WHAT'S THAT?

WE RETURN EXCALIBUR TO THE LADY OF THE LAKE.

WE TELL HER OF HER TRUE LOVE'S *DEATH.*

AND THEN WE *MOURN* TOGETHER.

WAKE UP.

COME **ON**, WE DON'T HAVE ALL DAY.

WHAT, YOU DON'T THINK THAT **DYING** ON ME IS GOING TO GET YOU OUT OF OUR **AGREEMENT**, DO YOU?

BRAN, WHAT ARE YOU **DOING** HERE? I'M STILL ALIVE? BUT **HOW**?

REBORN, MORE LIKE. BLAME MERLIN AND NIMUE.

THEY CONVINCED MORGANA TO PLACE A SHARD OF **CALIBURN** INTO MORDRED'S SPEAR SO WHEN IT KILLED YOU, IT ALSO **HEALED** YOU.

I SHOULD TELL EVERYONE . . .

NO, ARTHUR, YOUR TIME **HERE** IS OVER. YOU KNOW THIS IS TRUE.

YOUR VISION **STOPPED** HERE. AS DOES YOUR **KINGSHIP**.

YOUR MORTAL VOWS AND OATHS ARE FULFILLED. YOU'RE **FREE**, ARTHUR.

FREE TO **RULE AVALON** WHILE I TRAVEL. FREE TO FIND **NEW** LOVE.

SHE **WAITS** FOR YOU, YOU KNOW.

SAIL TO HER. AND I'LL SEE YOU WHEN I RETURN.

BUT I'M JUST NOT SURE THAT *THIS* IS THE RIGHT COURSE OF ACTION!

THAT'S THE *THIRD TIME* YOU'VE SAID THAT.

JUST *THROW* THE DAMNED THING!

ALL RIGHT. BUT I *STILL* THINK WE SHOULD HAVE KEPT IT!

LADY OF THE LAKE! WE RETURN YOUR SWORD!

SPLASH!

I EXPECTED SOMETHING *BIGGER*.

COME, WE FULFILLED THE PROMISE. WE HAVE A *KINGDOM* TO REBUILD.

THE SAXONS WILL STILL NEED TO BE *STOPPED*, AND WE NEED TO FIND MERLIN, DISCOVER WHAT *HAPPENED* TO MORGANA—

EVERYONE! LOOK AT THE *WATER!*

ARTHUR GOES *HOME.*

AS SHOULD WE ALL. WE HAVE *DEAD* TO BURY...

...AND *HEROES* TO SING GREAT SONGS OF.

CAN WE NOT GO ANY *FASTER*?

WHY? ARE YOU IN A *HURRY* TO REACH AVALON? TO LEAVE THIS *MORTAL REALM*?

AS A MATTER OF FACT, *YES*. FOR THE FIRST TIME, MY LIFE ISN'T PRE-DETERMINED.

FOR THE FIRST TIME, I CAN TRULY *EMBRACE* LOVE.

AND WILL THIS LOVE EMBRACE YOU *BACK*?

I HOPE SO. I WISH FOR NOTHING *MORE* SO, AND HAVE DONE FOR *YEARS*.

BUT WHAT WILL *HAPPEN* WHEN I GET TO AVALON? WHAT WILL SHE SAY WHEN I *BEG HER* TO BE MY *QUEEN*?

WELL, I THINK SHE'D BE A *FOOL* TO SAY NO TO SUCH AN OFFER.

VIVIANNE! MY LOVE! SO *LONG* HAVE I YEARNED TO SPEAK THOSE WORDS!

AND SO LONG HAVE I YEARNED TO *HEAR* THEM, MY KING.

SHOULDN'T YOU BE *STEERING THE BOAT* THOUGH? WE COULD END UP *ANYWHERE*!

YOU FOOL. I'M THE *LADY OF THE LAKE*.

THIS BOAT GOES WHEREVER I *TELL* IT TO. AND RIGHT NOW, MY KING --

-- IT'S *TAKING US HOME*.

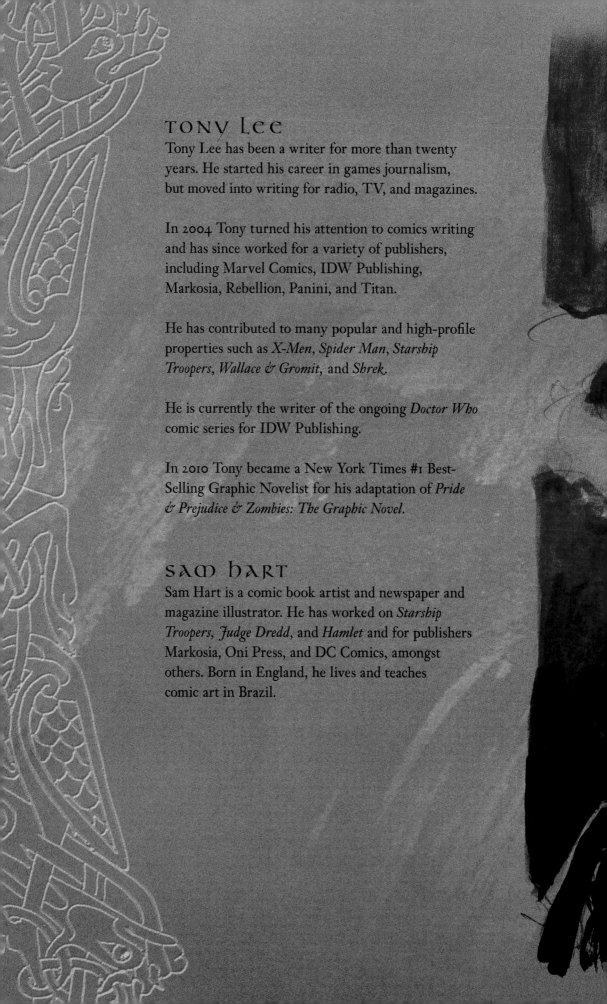

TONY LEE

Tony Lee has been a writer for more than twenty years. He started his career in games journalism, but moved into writing for radio, TV, and magazines.

In 2004 Tony turned his attention to comics writing and has since worked for a variety of publishers, including Marvel Comics, IDW Publishing, Markosia, Rebellion, Panini, and Titan.

He has contributed to many popular and high-profile properties such as *X-Men*, *Spider Man*, *Starship Troopers*, *Wallace & Gromit*, and *Shrek*.

He is currently the writer of the ongoing *Doctor Who* comic series for IDW Publishing.

In 2010 Tony became a New York Times #1 Best-Selling Graphic Novelist for his adaptation of *Pride & Prejudice & Zombies: The Graphic Novel*.

SAM HART

Sam Hart is a comic book artist and newspaper and magazine illustrator. He has worked on *Starship Troopers*, *Judge Dredd*, and *Hamlet* and for publishers Markosia, Oni Press, and DC Comics, amongst others. Born in England, he lives and teaches comic art in Brazil.

To Tracy, my Muse and Inspiration.
And Doreen Lee, the first and best editor
I ever had. Rest In Peace, Mum.
T. L.

To all my teachers ever, for the classes,
books and conversation.
And to Fabi.
S. H.

Copyright © 2011 by Tony Lee
Illustrations copyright © 2011 by Sam Hart

First U.S. edition 2011

Library of Congress Cataloging-in-Publication Data is available.

Library of Congress Catalog Card Number pending

ISBN 978-0-7636-4644-8 (hardcover)
ISBN 978-0-7636-4643-1 (paperback)
ISBN 978-0-7636-6244-8 (Scholastic paperback)

11 12 13 14 15 16 SWT 10 9 8 7 6 5 4 3 2 1

Printed in Dongguan, Guangdong, China

This book was typeset in Wild Words and Archetype.
The illustrations were created digitally.

This edition is only available for distribution through the school market.

Candlewick Press
99 Dover Street
Somerville, Massachusetts 02144

visit us at www.candlewick.com